Curious George Can Go, Go, Go

Written by Francie Alexander

Houghton Mifflin Harcourt
Boston   New York

There are many places
to go!
There are many ways
to move.

We go to school.
We can walk to school.
We can ride to school.

PUMPKIN
PATCH

We can go to a farm.
We can ride a pony.
We go on a hayride.
We can run in the pumpkin
patch.

The man and George drive to the city.

Many people are on the go, go, go.

Some people walk.

Some people ride.

They ride in cars and buses
and trains.

The man and George are going on a trip.
They come to the airport.

They will walk.
And they will ride.

Then they will fly.

Up, up, and away!